ScottForesman

D'Nealian® Handwriting

Third Edition

Book **3**

Author
Donald Neal Thurber

ScottForesman

A Division of HarperCollins*Publishers*

Editorial Offices: Glenview, Illinois
Regional Offices: Sunnyvale, California • Tucker, Georgia
Glenview, Illinois • Oakland, New Jersey • Dallas, Texas

Acknowledgments

Text
page 73: From "Louella's Song" by Eloise Greenfield. Granted by permission of Marie Brown Associates, copyright © 1975 by Eloise Greenfield.
page 99: From *Kate Shelley and the Midnight Express* by Margaret K. Wetterer, copyright 1990 by Carolrhoda Books, Inc., 241 First Avenue North, Minneapolis, MN 55401. Used with permission of the publisher.
page 125: From *Company's Coming* by Arthur Yorinks. Text copyright © 1988 by Arthur Yorinks, Illustrations copyright © 1988 by David Small. Reprinted by permission of Crown Publishers, Inc.

Illustrations
Lois Axeman 22, 34, 35, 37, 40, 55; Leslie Bowman 19; Judith dufour-Love 25, 26, 27, 31; Lane Gregory 56, 65, 70, 119; Konrad Hock 102, 103, 107, 108; Gary Hoover 85; Cheryl Kirk-Noll 18, 21, 50; Richard Kriegler 114; Yoshi Miyake 52, 53, 72, 82, 83, 121; James Needham 12, 13, 14, 15; Jan Spivey Gilchrist 73; Judy Sakaguchi 23; Cindy Salans-Rosenheim 86; Carol Schwartz 16, 17; Jeff Severn 8; Lena Shiffman 80, 81; Georgia Shola 9, 59, 110, 111; Susan Swan 33; Andrea Tochiera 66, 67, 69, 104, 105; Jenny Vainisi 39; Dana Verkouteren 99; Jack Wallen 28; Darcy Whitehead 3, 4, 5, 11, 29, 49, 57, 58, 73, 77, 78, 79, 99, 124, 125

Photographs
Camerique, 89, 115, 122; H. Armstrong Roberts/B. Taylor, 47; H. Armstrong Roberts/M. Barrett, 88; H. Armstrong Roberts/G.L. French, 92; H. Armstrong Roberts/J. Blank, 93; H. Armstrong Roberts, 95; H. Armstrong Roberts/Uselmann, 96; H. Armstrong Roberts, 112, 113; Image Bank/Mitchell Funk, 117; NASA, 116, 120; Photo Researchers, 61; Photo Researchers/Lawrence Migdale, 63; Tom Stock/Stuart Westmorland, 95; Super Stock, 91; Tony Stone Worldwide, 36; Tony Stone Worldwide/Charles McNaulty, 42; Tony Stone Worldwide, 43; Tony Stone Worldwide/Peter Carrez, 47; Tony Stone Worldwide/Jan Lukas, 61; Tony Stone Worldwide/Robert E Daemmrich, 62; Tony Stone Worldwide/Jan Riley, 95

Staff Credits
Editorial: Marianne Hiland, Gerry Murphy-Ferguson, Delores Nemo, and Wendy Wallen
Design: Paula Meyers
Production: Barbara Albright and Maryann Lewis
Marketing: Sue Cowden and Kristine Stanczak

D'Nealian® Handwriting is a registered trademark of Donald Neal Thurber.

ISBN: 0-673-28532-4
Copyright © 1993
Scott, Foresman and Company, Glenview, Illinois
All Rights Reserved. Printed in the United States of America.

1415-WEB-0099

Contents

5 Unit One: Getting Ready to Write
6 Left-handed Position for Writing
7 Right-handed Position for Writing
8 Letter Size and Form
9 Letter Slant and Spacing
10 Cursive is Coming

11 Unit Two: Reviewing Manuscript Letters
12 Using Numbers in a List
13 Writing Manuscript **aA, dD, oO,** and **gG**
14 Writing Manuscript **cC, eE,** and **sS**
15 Writing Manuscript **fF, bB,** and **lL**
16 Writing Manuscript **tT, hH,** and **kK**
17 Writing Manuscript **iI, uU, wW,** and **yY**
18 Writing Manuscript **jJ, rR, nN, mM,** and **pP**
19 Writing Manuscript **qQ, vV, zZ,** and **xX**
20 Practice
21 Review
22 Evaluation
23 Making a Schedule
24 Here's Cursive
25 Strokes That Make Cursive Letters

29 Unit Three: Writing Lower-case Cursive Letters
30 Letter Size and Form
31 Letter Slant and Word Spacing
32 Writing Cursive **l, h, k,** and **t**
34 Writing Cursive **i, u,** and **e**
36 Writing Cursive **j** and **p**
38 Practice
39 Review
40 Evaluation
41 Filling Out a Form
42 Writing Cursive **a, d,** and **c**
44 Writing Cursive **n, m,** and **x**
46 Writing Cursive **g, y,** and **q**
48 Practice
49 Review
50 Evaluation

51 Writing a Postcard
52 Writing Cursive **o, w,** and **b**
54 Practice
55 Review
56 Evaluation
57 Making a List
58 Making a Poster
59 Writing Titles and Authors
60 Writing Cursive **v** and **z**
62 Writing Cursive **s** and **r**
64 Writing Cursive **f**
66 Joining Sidestroke Letters
68 Practice
69 Review
70 Evaluation
71 Writing Number Words and Time
72 Writing Number Words
73 Reading and Writing
76 Writing Numbers in a Paragraph

77 **Unit Four: Writing Capital Cursive Letters**
78 Letter Size and Form
79 Letter Slant
80 Writing Cursive **A** and **C**
82 Writing Cursive **E** and **O**
84 Practice
85 Review
86 Evaluation
87 Letter, Word, and Sentence Spacing
88 Writing Cursive **H** and **K**
90 Writing Cursive **N, M,** and **U**
92 Writing Cursive **V, W,** and **Y**
94 Practice
95 Review
96 Evaluation
97 Writing a Thank-you Note
98 Addressing an Envelope
99 Reading and Writing
102 Writing Cursive **T** and **F**
104 Writing Cursive **B, P,** and **R**
106 Practice
107 Review
108 Evaluation
109 Writing Punctuation Marks
110 Writing a Telephone Message
111 Writing Abbreviations
112 Writing Cursive **G, S,** and **I**
114 Writing Cursive **Q, Z,** and **D**
116 Writing Cursive **J, X,** and **L**
118 Practice
119 Review
120 Evaluation
121 Writing Names of Planets
122 Making a Chart
124 Signing an Autograph Book
125 Reading and Writing
128 Index

Unit One
Getting Ready to Write

Left-handed Position for Writing

Sit tall with both feet on the floor. Rest both arms on your desk.

Your paper should slant from the right at the top to the left at the bottom. Rest your right hand on the paper to hold it in place.

Hold the pencil lightly between your thumb and index finger. Look at the picture to see how. The eraser end of the pencil should point toward your left shoulder.

Right-handed Position for Writing

Sit tall with both feet on the floor. Rest both arms on your desk.

Your paper should slant from the left at the top to the right at the bottom. Rest your left hand on the paper to hold it in place.

Hold the pencil lightly between your thumb and index finger. Look at the picture to see how. The eraser end of the pencil should point toward your right shoulder.

a c e i m n o r s u v w x z
b d f h k l t
g j p q y

Manuscript letters have only three sizes. There are small letters, tall letters, and letters with descenders.

Small letters sit on the bottom line. They touch the middle line. Write three small letters.

Tall letters also sit on the bottom line. They touch the top line. Write three tall letters.

Letters with descenders are **g, j, p, q,** and **y.** These letters have tails that go down under the bottom line. The descenders touch the line below. Write three letters with descenders.

Forming letters correctly helps make handwriting easy to read. Some letters, like **b, d, o,** and **g,** must be closed. The letters **t** and **f** must be crossed. Dot the letters **i** and **j.**

Can you read the phrase below?

biggest dog

The phrase is **biggest dog.** Why is it so hard to read?

Write the phrase **biggest dog** correctly.

Is your phrase easier to read?

8

Letter Slant and Spacing

Slant all your letters the same way. That will make your handwriting easier to read. Find the slant that is right for you. Then keep that slant.

Some writers slant their letters to the right.

right

Some writers slant their letters to the left.

left

Some writers make their letters straight up and down.

up and down

Do not slant your letters different ways.

different

Which handwriting is hard to read? Why is it hard?

Spacing is important. Letters and words should not be too close together or too far apart. Write this sentence. Use correct spacing.

Letme   outo fhere!

Cursive Is Coming

People may write messages, lists, and other information in two ways. Read the two lists below. Some letters look almost the same in both lists.

A letter is circled in each list that looks almost the same. Circle three more letters that look almost the same in cursive and in manuscript.

Manuscript
You already know how to write like this.

Cursive
You will soon learn how to write like this.

Ms. Jensen's Class
Favorite Pets

cat
dog
hamster
fish
bird

Ms. Jensen's Class
Favorite Pets

cat
dog
hamster
fish
bird

Unit Two
Reviewing Manuscript Letters

Using Numbers in a List

Mrs. Matoba's class is having a pet show. Write in manuscript the list of pets entered in the show. Line up all the numbers in the list. Follow each number with a period.

Pet Show

1. Mittens
2. Casey
3. Felix
4. Gus
5. Bingo
6. Dudley
7. Spot
8. Buttons
9. Muffy
10. Dusty

Writing Manuscript aA, dD, oO, and gG

Write the lower-case letters.

a   a

d   d

o   o

g   g

Write the capital letters.

A   D   O   G

Write the names.

Great Dane

Atlas Dog Obedience

Writing Manuscript cC, eE, and sS

Write the lower-case letters.

c   c

e   e

s   s

Write the capital letters.

C   E   S

Write the names.

Cocker Spaniel

Edgar's Dog Grooming

Old English Sheepdog

Writing Manuscript fF, bB, and lL

Write the lower-case letters.

f   f

b   b

l   l

Write the capital letters.

F   B   L

Write the names.

Libby

Fluffy

Barkley   **Lassie**

Fido's Biscuits

Writing Manuscript tT, hH, and kK

Happy Trails Kennel

Write the lower-case letters.

t   *t*

h   *h*

k   *k*

Write the capital letters.

T   *H*   *K*

Write the names and the sentence.

King

Tuffy

Take Heidi to the Happy Trails Kennel.

16

a b c d e f g h i j k l m

n o p q r s t u v w x y z

A B C D E F G

H I J K L M N O P Q

R S T U V W X Y Z

a b c d e f g h i j k

l m n o p q r s t

u v w x y z , ' . ? " " !

A B C D E F G H I

J K L M N O P 2 R

S T U V W X Y Z

1 2 3 4 5 6 7 8 9 10

Samples of printing & cursive

Writing Manuscript iI, uU, wW, and yY

Write the lower-case letters.

i   *i*

u   *u*

w   *w*

y   *y*

Write the capital letters.

I   U   W   Y

Write the sentence.

Yes, Uncle Willie and I saw a cute puppy.

Writing Manuscript jJ, rR, nN, mM, and pP

Write the lower-case letters.

j   j

r   r

n   n

m   m

p   p

Write the capital letters.

J   R   N

M   P

Write the sentence.

Poodles run and jump.

Writing Manuscript qQ, vV, zZ, and xX

Write the lower-case letters.

q   q

v   v

z   z

x   x

Write the capital letters.

Q   V   Z   X

Write the sentence.

Liz and Xavier McQueen pose with Max and Zeus.

Practice

Write the lower-case manuscript letters in alphabetical order.

a b c d e f g h i
j k l m n o p q r
s t u v w x y z

Write the capital manuscript letters in alphabetical order.

A B C D E F G
H I J K L M N
O P Q R S T U
V W X Y Z

20

Review

Write the words.

tub

Pixie

soap

puppy

Gloria

brushes

Jeff

towels

Evaluation

Remember: Slant all your letters the same way.

Write the words and sentences.

Dog Washing Today

_____

_____

_____

_____

Zack will shampoo.

_____

_____

_____

_____

Rinse the puppy quickly.

_____

_____

_____

_____

Jeff likes to dry.

_____

_____

_____

Check Your Handwriting   Yes   No
Do all your letters slant the same way?   ☐   ☐

Making a Schedule

The Harrises are going away for the weekend. Sarah will take care of their dog, Gus, while they are away. Mrs. Harris made a schedule to help Sarah remember what to do.

8:00 A.M.	Walk Gus and feed him breakfast. Give him fresh water.
1:00 P.M.	Take Gus for a walk. Play fetch.
6:00 P.M.	Feed Gus dinner. Brush him and walk him.
9:00 P.M.	Walk Gus. Give him a dog treat. Say Goodnight.

Copy the schedule. Write as straight across as you can even though there are no writing lines on the schedule. Be sure to adjust the size of your handwriting to fit the space.

Here's Cursive

You know how to write manuscript letters. Now you will learn to write cursive letters. What types of writing will you do in cursive?

I'm writing to my favorite basketball player to ask for his autograph.

I'm practicing my signature for signing autographs when I'm famous.

Two Ways to Write

Look closely at the two sentences below. One is in manuscript, and the other is in cursive. Circle the letters that look almost the same in manuscript and cursive. Most cursive letters are joined together. Make a ⌣ under five places where the letters are joined. The first one is done for you.

Manuscript	Cursive
I like	I like
cursive.	cursive.

Strokes That Make Cursive Letters

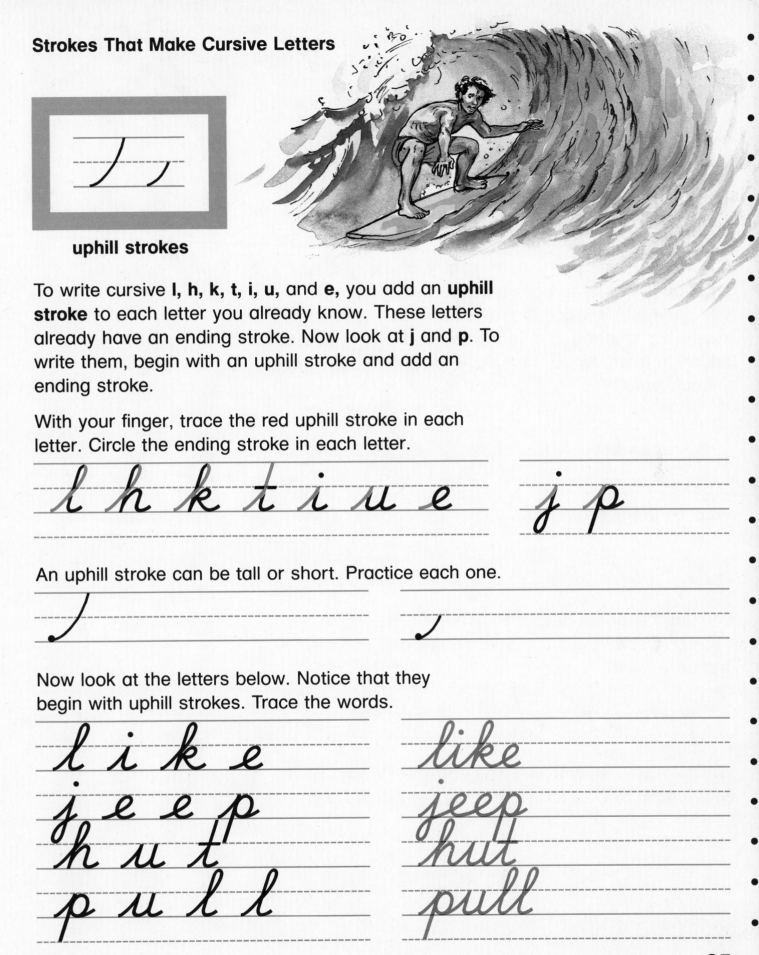

uphill strokes

To write cursive **l, h, k, t, i, u,** and **e,** you add an **uphill stroke** to each letter you already know. These letters already have an ending stroke. Now look at **j** and **p**. To write them, begin with an uphill stroke and add an ending stroke.

With your finger, trace the red uphill stroke in each letter. Circle the ending stroke in each letter.

l h k t i u e   j p

An uphill stroke can be tall or short. Practice each one.

Now look at the letters below. Notice that they begin with uphill strokes. Trace the words.

like   like

jeep   jeep

hut   hut

pull   pull

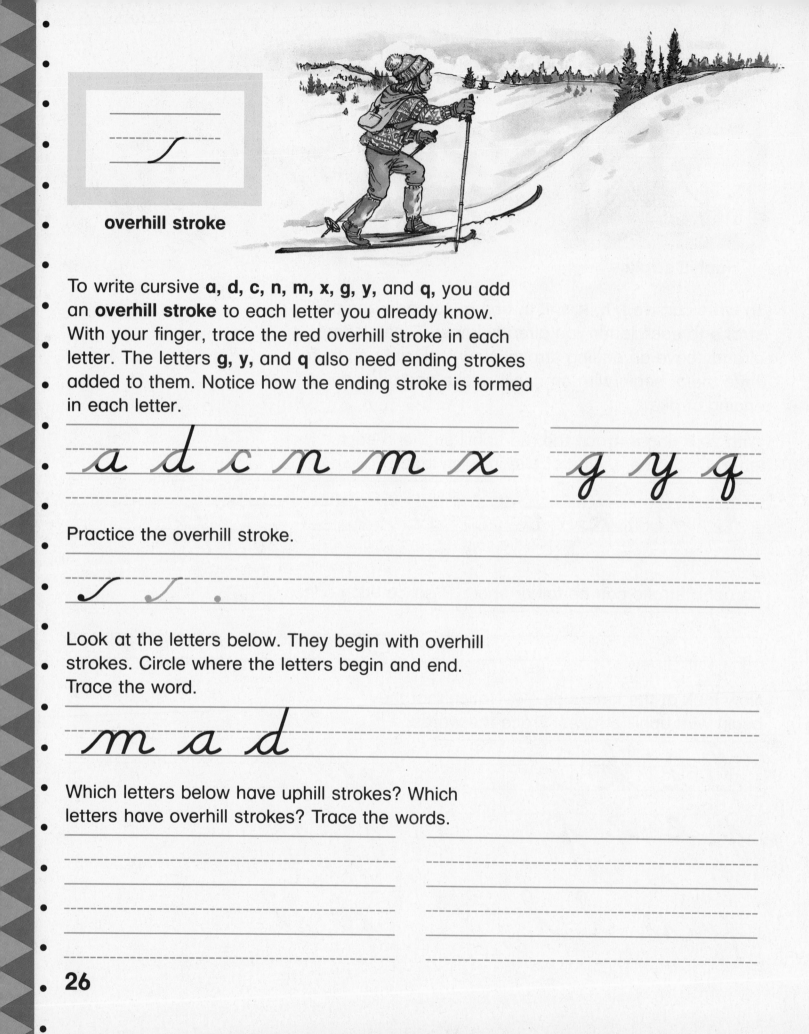

overhill stroke

To write cursive **a, d, c, n, m, x, g, y,** and **q,** you add an **overhill stroke** to each letter you already know. With your finger, trace the red overhill stroke in each letter. The letters **g, y,** and **q** also need ending strokes added to them. Notice how the ending stroke is formed in each letter.

Practice the overhill stroke.

Look at the letters below. They begin with overhill strokes. Circle where the letters begin and end. Trace the word.

Which letters below have uphill strokes? Which letters have overhill strokes? Trace the words.

26

sidestroke

The letters **o, w,** and **b** end with a **sidestroke.** Which letter begins with an overhill stroke? Which two letters begin with uphill strokes? With your finger, trace the red sidestroke in each letter.

o w b

Practice the sidestroke.

Look at the letters below. Notice where they begin and end. A sidestroke letter always joins the following letter near the middle line. This changes the beginning stroke of the following letter. Notice how the sidestroke changes **n, e,** and **a** in **on, wet,** and **bat.** Trace the words.

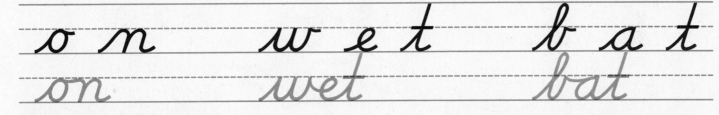

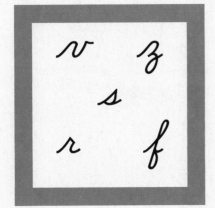

The letters **v, z, s, r,** and **f** are special because they look different from the letters you already know. Which letter ends with a sidestroke? Which two letters begin with overhill strokes? Which three letters begin with uphill strokes? Trace the letters **v, z, s, r,** and **f.**

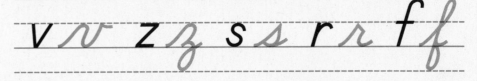

The words below have all of the joining strokes you learned. Find five letters that begin with **uphill strokes.** Find four letters that begin with **overhill strokes.** Find three letters that end with **sidestrokes.** Then trace the words.

sly
quick
fox

jumps
over
dog

Read the following sentences.

I am ready to write in cursive. Are you?

Unit Three

Writing Lower-case Cursive Letters

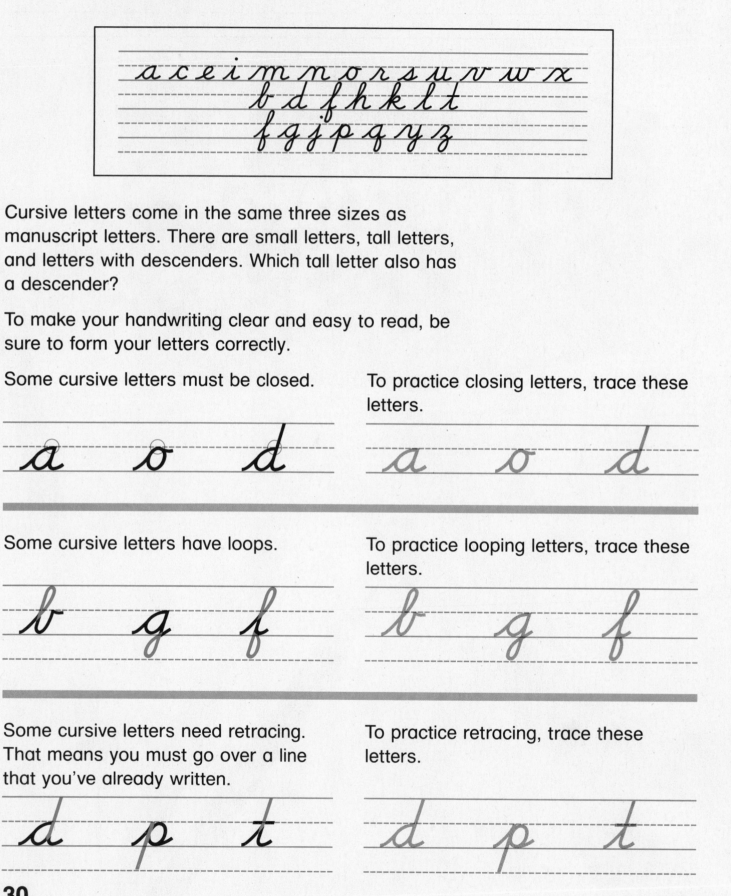

Cursive letters come in the same three sizes as manuscript letters. There are small letters, tall letters, and letters with descenders. Which tall letter also has a descender?

To make your handwriting clear and easy to read, be sure to form your letters correctly.

Some cursive letters must be closed.

To practice closing letters, trace these letters.

Some cursive letters have loops.

To practice looping letters, trace these letters.

Some cursive letters need retracing. That means you must go over a line that you've already written.

To practice retracing, trace these letters.

Letter Slant and Word Spacing

When you write in cursive, slant all your letters the same way. You may slant your letters to the right or to the left. You may write them straight up and down. Do not slant your letters different ways.

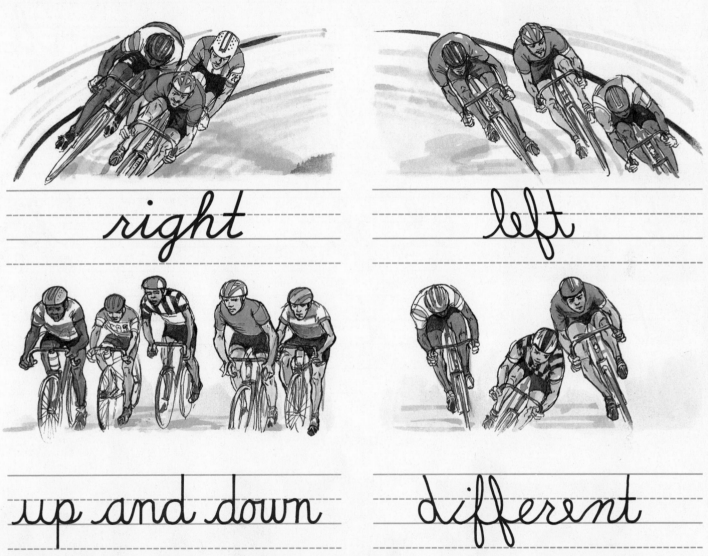

right

left

up and down

different

Which writing is hard to read? Why is it hard?

Use correct spacing when you write. The letters in a word should be evenly spaced. Leave more space between words than between letters in a word.

aredbike

a red bike

Which writing is easier to read? Why is it easier?

Writing Cursive l, h, k, and t

Cursive letters **l, h, k,** and **t** look like their manuscript forms. Add an uphill stroke to write the cursive letter. Trace and write the letters.

Amy has a collection of letters. Write each letter in cursive.

l _____   h _____   k _____   t _____

When you write in cursive, you join the letters. Most
letters join at the bottom line. Trace and write the
joined letters.

ll ll   ll
lh lh   lh
lk lk   lk
lt lt   lt
hh hh   hh
hl hl   hl
ht ht   ht
kl kl   kl
tt tt   tt
tl tl   tl
th th   th

kite   hut   lei   tree

33

Writing Cursive i, u, and e

Cursive letters **i, u,** and **e** look like their manuscript forms. Add an uphill stroke to write the cursive letter. Trace and write the letters.

Trace and write the words.

it

it

hull

hull

let

let

hi

hi

kite

kite

tell

tell

Trace and write the words and phrases.

hit

hit

hut

hut

hill

hill

lei

lei

tie

tie

till

till

like the hike

like the hike

the little ukulele

the little ukulele

Writing Cursive j and p

Cursive letters **j** and **p** look very much like their manuscript forms. To write them in cursive, you must add an uphill stroke <u>and</u> an ending stroke. Trace and write the letters.

j j   *j j .*   *j*

p p   *p p .*   *p*

Trace and write the words.

jet

jet

pet

pet

peek

peek

up

up

help

help

keep

keep

Trace and write the words and phrases.

jut

jut

up

up

put

put

jeep

jeep

pull

pull

peel

peel

the little jet

the little jet

like the pup

like the pup

37

Practice

Write the cursive letters.

l   *l*

h   *h*

k   *k*

t   *t*

i   *i*

u   *u*

e   *e*

j   *j*

p   *p*

Circle your best letter in each line.

Practice joining the letters below.

ju   *pl*

ue   *et*

ul   *li*

Review

Write the words.

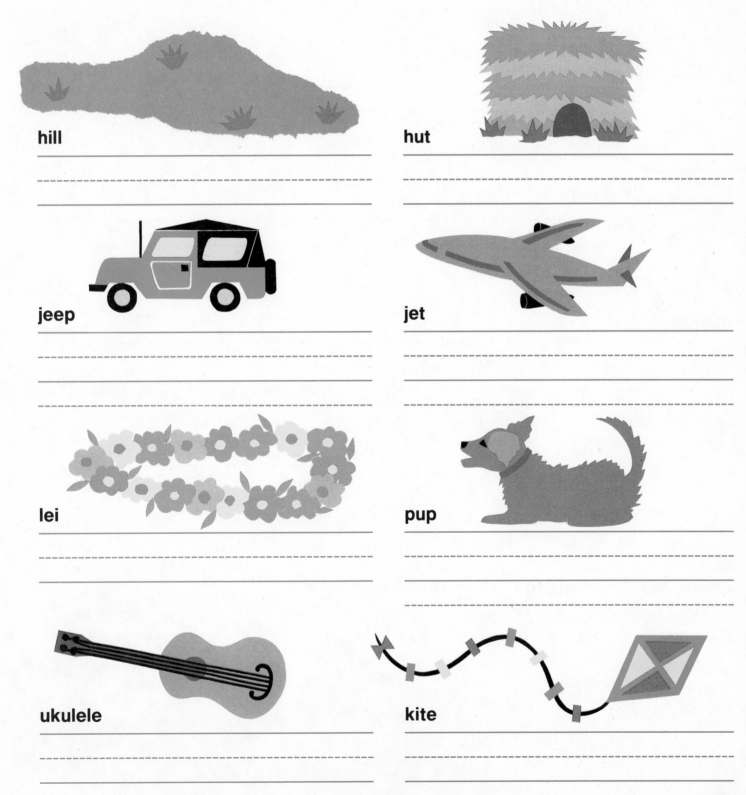

hill

hut

jeep

jet

lei

pup

ukulele

kite

39

Evaluation

Remember: Cross the letter **t** and dot the letters **i** and **j**.

Write the phrases.

the hike uphill

_____

_____

----

like the jeep

_____

_____

the little hut

_____

----

kept the pup

_____

_____

Check Your Handwriting   Yes   No
Did you cross the letter **t**?   ☐   ☐
Did you dot the letters **i** and **j**? ☐   ☐

Filling Out a Form

Before you fill out a form, read it carefully.
Then follow the directions given.

```
Hawaii Volcanoes National Park
Please send me information about special events at the Visitors' Center.
                    I am interested in:

[X] Birdwatching        [ ] Exhibits          [ ] Nature walks

Please print.

Name  Tanaka              Julie                    E.
      Last                First                    Middle Initial

Address  646              Waiholo Drive            2A
         Number           Street                   Apt. No.

      Honolulu            Hawaii                   96821
      City                State                    Zip Code
```

Fill out the form below with your name and address.
You may have to adjust the size of your handwriting to
fit the space. When a form tells you to "print," it means
you should use manuscript handwriting.

```
Hawaii Volcanoes National Park
Please send me information about special events at the Visitors' Center.
                    I am interested in:

[ ] Birdwatching        [ ] Exhibits          [ ] Nature walks

Please print.


Name  _____
      Last                First                    Middle Initial

Address _____
        Number           Street                   Apt. Number

      _____
      City                State                    ZIP Code
```

Writing Cursive a, d, and c

Cursive letters **a, d,** and **c** look like their manuscript forms. Add an overhill stroke to write the cursive letter. Trace and write the letters.

a a a .   *a*

d d d .   *d*

c c c .   *c*

Trace and write the words.

at

at

cap

cap

dad

dad

all

all

lake

lake

cut

cut

Trace and write the phrases.

a little child

a little child

the path ahead

the path ahead

packed a peach

packed a peach

the apple juice

the apple juice

Writing Cursive n, m, and x

Cursive letters **n, m,** and **x** look like their manuscript forms. Add an overhill stroke to write the cursive letter. Trace and write the letters.

n n　　　*n n.*　　　　　*n*

m m　　　*m m.*　　　　　*m*

x x　　　*x x.*　　　　　*x*

Trace and write the words.

can

can

ham

ham

lunch

lunch

taxi

taxi

milk

milk

meat

meat

Trace and write the phrases.

lettuce and pickle

lettuce and pickle

mixed the chicken

mixed the chicken

the next picnic

the next picnic

elm and maple

elm and maple

Writing Cursive g, y, and q

Cursive letters **g**, **y**, and **q** look like their manuscript forms. To write them in cursive, you must add an overhill stroke <u>and</u> an ending stroke. Trace and write the letters.

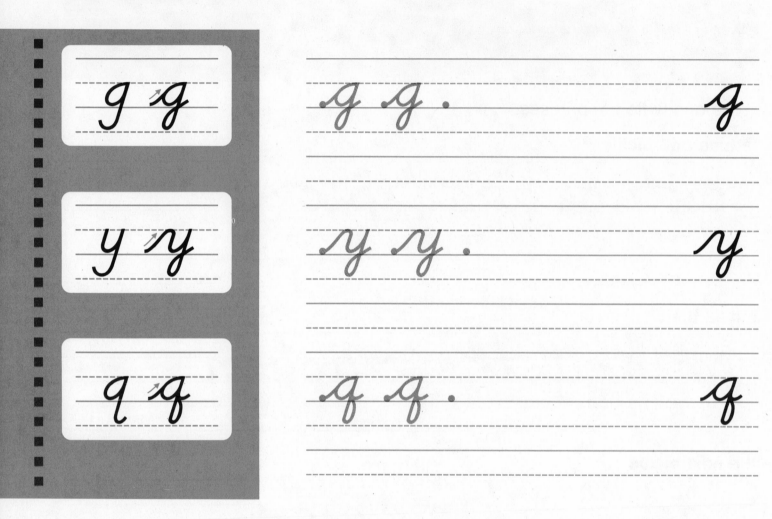

Trace and write the words.

my

my

quit

quit

light

light

Trace and write the phrases.

a jungle gym

a jungle gym

playing tag

playing tag

a quick game

a quick game

happy in the city

happy in the city

Practice

Write the cursive letters.

a   *a*

d   *d*

c   *c*

n   *n*

m   *m*

x   *x*

g   *g*

y   *y*

q   *q*

Circle your best letter in each line.

Practice joining the letters below.

ay   *qu*

ge   *da*

an   *ix*

48

Review

Write the words and phrases.

picnic

_____

- - - - - - - - - - - - -

_____

game

_____

- - - - - - - - - - - - -

_____

taxi

_____

- - - - - - - - - - - - -

_____

ham

_____

- - - - - - - - - - - - -

_____

a quacking duck

_____

- - - - - - - - - - - - -

_____

a yellow kitten

_____

- - - - - - - - - - - - -

_____

Evaluation

Remember: Descenders should touch the line below.

Write the phrases.

the next meal

a picnic at night

hugging a child

the cuddly quilt

Check Your Handwriting

Do your descenders touch the line below?

Yes   No

Writing a Postcard

There is very little space on a postcard. You must write small, form your letters clearly, and keep your lines straight. Manuscript is often clearer than cursive when you have to write small.

When you address an envelope or a postcard, use all capital manuscript letters and no punctuation marks. Abbreviate words like *Street* and *Apartment*, and the name of the state.

Dear Kathy,
    We are having lots of fun camping. Yesterday we hiked around the lake. Today we went swimming. Later, Dad and I caught some fish.
               Your friend,
               Jean Anne

MISS KATHRYN SCHULTZ
501 FARGO ST APT 320
CHICAGO IL 60626

Copy the postcard in manuscript.

Writing Cursive o, w, and b

You can see manuscript **o** and **w** in cursive **o** and **w**.
Cursive **b** looks very much like manuscript **b.** Begin
cursive **o** with an overhill stroke. Begin cursive **w** and **b**
with an uphill stroke. Each letter ends with a sidestroke
near the middle line. Trace and write the letters.

Remember that **o, w,** and **b** join the next letter near the
middle line. This changes the beginning stroke of the
next letter. Trace and write the joined letters and words.

bow

owl

wow

Ogden School has a lost-and-found box near the office. These are some of the items in the lost and found. Trace and write the phrases.

yellow woolen mitten

yellow woolen mitten

one black boot

one black boot

a blue and white cap

a blue and white cap

a big yellow bow

a big yellow bow

Practice

Write the letters.

_o_   _o_

_w_   _w_

_b_   _b_

Circle your best letter in each line.

Remember that **o, w,** and **b** join the letters that follow them near the middle line. Practice joining these letters.

_oo_   _oo_

_oy_   _oy_

_wi_   _wi_

_wa_   _wa_

_we_   _we_

_bi_   _bi_

_ba_   _ba_

_be_   _be_

Review

Write the words and the phrase.

wallet

book

boot

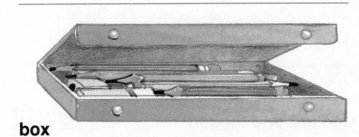

box

belt

watch

an old blue bike

Evaluation

Remember: Most letters in words are joined at the bottom line. The letters **o, w,** and **b** join the next letter near the middle line.

Write the phrases.

my new black and yellow notebook

looked and looked

below the window

Check Your Handwriting
Are the letters in your words joined correctly?

Yes   No

56

Making a List

Mrs. Jordan's class made a list of the items in the Lost and Found. They put the list on the bulletin board in the hall where everyone could see it. Copy the items on the list. Use cursive handwriting. Plan your space so that each item fits on one line. Make sure your sidestroke letters are joined correctly.

Lost and Found

one black boot   a ballpoint pen
one pink mitten   one yellow pencil
a yellow wool hat   a pink notebook
a new book   an old watch
a ball and mitt   a blue coat

Making a Poster

Liz and Marta made a poster to tell people about the Lincoln School Book Fair. They wanted to tell the time, the date, and the place. This is how it looked.

Copy the poster in manuscript handwriting. Be sure to write larger than you usually do.

Book Fair
Friday, May 17
10:00 A.M. to 3:00 P.M.
Lincoln School Gym
Come to the Fair!

Writing Titles and Authors

These are some of the books the third-graders bought at the Book Fair. Write the titles and authors in manuscript. Be sure to leave enough space between words, and underline a title when you write it.

<u>**Ramona, the Pest**</u> **by Beverly Cleary**

<u>**Everett Anderson's Friend**</u> **by Lucille Clifton**

<u>**The Boy and the Ghost**</u> **by Robert San Souci**

<u>**Storm in the Night**</u> **by Mary Stolz**

Writing Cursive v and z

Cursive **v** and **z** do not look like manuscript **v** and **z**.
Notice that cursive **v** ends with a sidestroke. Trace
and write the letters.

Remember that **v** joins the next letter near the
middle line. Trace and write the words.

violin

violin

move

move

van

van

buzz

buzz

lazy

lazy

zip

zip

Trace and write the phrases.

a lovely event

a lovely event

a lazy, hazy evening

a lazy, hazy evening

a dozen people

a dozen people

lively jazz

lively jazz

Writing Cursive s and r

Cursive **s** and **r** do not look like manuscript **s** and **r**.
Trace and write the letters.

s s   *s s.*   *s*

r r   *r r.*   *r*

Trace and write the words.

strings

strings

sing

sing

songs

songs

rhythm

rhythm

Trace and write the phrases.

rock and roll

rock and roll

orchestra and chorus

orchestra and chorus

seven percussion instruments

seven percussion instruments

a crazy rhythm

a crazy rhythm

Writing Cursive f

Cursive **f** does not look like its manuscript form.
Trace and write the letter.

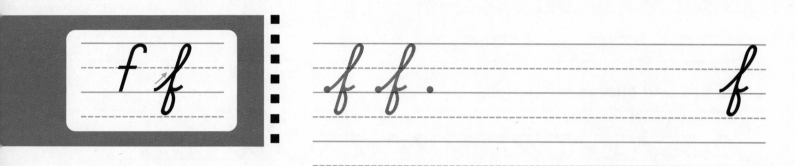

Trace and write the words and phrases.

fun

fun

fast

fast

first

first

treble clef

treble clef

bass clef

bass clef

Trace and write the phrases.

four friends on flutes

four friends on flutes

a good effort

a good effort

friendly faces

friendly faces

my favorite music

my favorite music

Joining Sidestroke Letters

The letters **o, w, b,** and **v** must join the next letter near the middle line. This changes the beginning stroke of the next letter. Trace and write the joined letters and words.

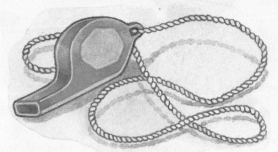

ba ba ba

tuba

ol ol ol

piccolo

wa wa wa

walk

bl bl bl

blue

or or or

uniform

wh wh wh

whistle

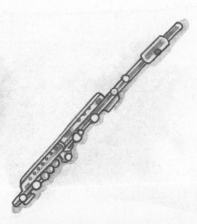

Trace and write the joined letters and words.

bu bu bu

bus

vi vi vi

viola

ov ov ov

ve ve ve

glove

ob ob ob

bo bo bo

oboe

oo oo oo

on on on

bassoon

om om om

trombone

Practice

Write the letters.

v v

z z

s s

r r

f f

Circle your best letter in each line.

Practice joining these letters.

vi vi

st st

sa sa

sh sh

fr fr

zz zz

Review

Write the words.

zither

harp

drums

violin

recorder

trumpet

saxophone

flute

Evaluation

Remember: Small letters should touch the middle line.

Write the phrases.

a symphony orchestra

lovely zither music

five pieces for the violin

Check Your Handwriting
Do your small letters touch the middle line?

Yes   No
☐   ☐

Writing Number Words and Time

Write the number words in cursive handwriting.
Remember to dot the letter **i** and cross the letter **t**.

zero

one

two

three

four

five

six

seven

eight

nine

ten

Beginning band practice is at 9:00, advanced band
practice is at 1:00, and chorus practice is at 3:00.
Write the times in numbers and words. Make sure your
numbers are the same size as your tall letters.

9:00   nine o'clock

1:00   one o'clock

3:00   three o'clock

Writing Number Words

An orchestra is made up of many instruments. Write the number and names of the instruments in the orchestra below. Make sure you form your letters clearly and make them the correct size.

twelve violins

_____

- -

_____

five cellos

_____

- -

_____

four flutes

_____

- -

_____

six clarinets

_____

- -

_____

two trumpets

_____

- -

_____

three drums

_____

- -

_____

Reading and Writing

In the story *Louella's Song,* Louella is a shy girl with a beautiful voice. When her teacher asks Louella to sing a solo, Louella panics. She does not want to sing by herself in front of an audience.

Read these paragraphs from the story to find out how Louella feels about singing in front of people.

Louella leaned forward in her seat and raised her hand. Of all the things in the world she didn't want to do, the thing she most of all didn't want to do was sing by herself, on a stage, in front of a lot of people. Everybody knew the song. She didn't know why Miss Simmons had to go and pick her!

She shook her hand in the air. "Miss Simmons," she said. "Miss Simmons, I can't sing by myself."

Miss Simmons looked up from the paper in her hand. "Yes you can, Louella," she said. "I know you've been trying to hide that sweet little voice, but I hear it every time we sing. All you have to do is sing out and make it a sweet big voice."

"But Miss Simmons . . .," Louella said.

Miss Simmons looked worried. "I've already planned the whole program," she said. "Please, Louella?"

Louella looked around the room for sympathy, but most of her classmates wouldn't look at her. And those who would were frowning. She had to say yes, but she didn't want to. She nodded her head at Miss Simmons, and everybody smiled. ■

Think about how you feel about performing in front of an audience. Many people are shy about performing, as Louella is. Other people love to perform. Write some words in the Word Bank below that might help you tell what you like or do not like about performing.

Word Bank

Samantha likes to perform in front of people. She wrote a paragraph telling what she likes about being in a play. Read her first two sentences.

It is fun to pretend. I like practicing with friends and playing a new part.

Read what Samantha wrote.   Yes   No
- Did she tell what she likes about being in a play?   ☐   ☐

Proofread Samantha's sentences.
- Are her letters closed correctly?   ☐   ☐
- Did she dot all her **i**'s?   ☐   ☐

Write Samantha's sentences on another sheet of paper. Be sure to close your letters correctly. Remember to dot all your **i**'s.

Now it's your turn to write. Write about what you like or do not like about performing in front of other people. You may want to use the words from your Word Bank.

_____

- -

_____

- -

_____

- -

_____

- -

_____

- -

_____

- -

_____

- -

Read your draft carefully.   Yes   No

- Did you write several things about performing that you like or do not like?   ☐   ☐

Proofread your work.

- Are your letters closed correctly?   ☐   ☐
- Did you dot the letters **i** and **j**?   ☐   ☐

Edit your copy. Then write your revised copy on another sheet of paper.

75

Writing Numbers in a Paragraph

Write out a number at the beginning of a sentence.
Write out numbers that are one or two words.

> Six hundred twenty students go to
> Hoffman School. Eighty-two are in beginning
> band, seventy-three are in advanced band, and
> ninety-seven are in chorus.

Copy the paragraph below. Use manuscript writing.
Remember to indent the first line.

Name

Unit Four
Writing Capital Cursive Letters

Letter Size and Form

Capital cursive letters all touch the top and bottom lines. Three capital letters also have descenders that touch the line below. To make your handwriting clear and easy to read, be sure to form your letters correctly.

Some capital letters must be closed.

$\mathcal{A}$ $\mathcal{P}$

You must retrace when you write some capital letters. That means you must go over a line you've already written.

$\mathcal{B}$ $\mathcal{n}$

Some capital letters have loops.

$\mathcal{D}$ $\mathcal{L}$

Some capital letters have descenders. The descenders should touch the line below.

$\mathcal{J}$ $\mathcal{Y}$

Look at the capital letters in the alphabet below. Circle four letters that must be closed. Underline five letters that have loops. Put a ✔ above two letters that have descenders. Put an **X** over four letters that have retracing.

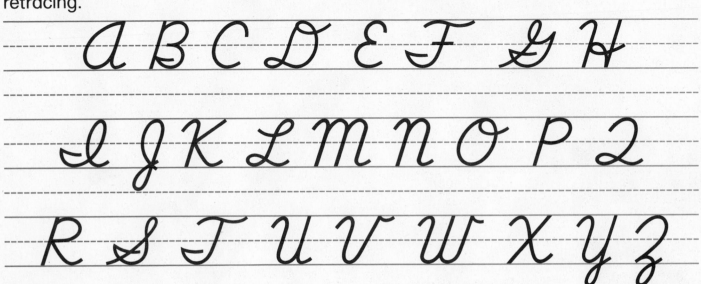

Letter Slant

Slant your capital letters in the same direction that you slant your lower-case letters. You may slant your letters to the right or to the left. You may write them straight up and down. Do not slant your capital letters differently from your lower-case letters.

Right

Left

Up and down

Different

Which writing is hard to read? Why is it hard?

Numbers and punctuation marks should slant in the same direction as your letters. Look at this sentence written two ways. Circle four letters that slant the wrong way in the first sentence. Then trace the correct sentence.

Will you come to lunch at 12:00?

Will you come to lunch at 12:00?

Write this phrase. Slant all your letters the same way.

the same slant

Do your letters all slant the same way?   Yes ☐   No ☐

Writing Cursive A and C

Capital cursive **A** looks different from manuscript **A**. Cursive **C** looks like its manuscript form. Trace and write the letters.

A A   a a   ·   a

C C   C C   ·   C

Trace and write the proper nouns. Always join **A** and **C** to the letters that follow them. Be sure to begin each proper noun with a capital. Put a comma between the name of a city and state.

Aspen, Colorado

Aspen, Colorado

Alex

Alex

Carmen

Carmen

Trace and write the sentences.

Anne's class visited Ace Computers.

Anne's class visited Ace Computers.

A guide named Cliff gave them a tour.

A guide named Cliff gave them a tour.

Andy and Carl liked the computers.

Andy and Carl liked the computers.

WELCOME TO ACE COMPUTER COMPANY

Writing Cursive E and O

Cursive **E** looks a little like manuscript **E**. You can see manuscript **O** in cursive **O**. Trace and write the letters.

Trace and write the proper nouns. Always join **E** to the letter that follows it, but do not join **O**.

Eugene, Oregon

Eugene, Oregon

Elsa

Elsa

Oliver

Oliver

Trace and write the sentences.

Open the program.

Open the program.

Olivia pressed Enter to begin.

Olivia pressed Enter to begin.

Otis and Eddie share computer E.

Otis and Eddie share computer E.

Practice

Write the letters.

a

C

E

O

Circle your best letter in each line.

Write the names of these places.

America

Canada

Alaska

California

Ohio

East Coast

Europe

Orient

Review

The computer screen shows the names of the students in Mrs. Olsen's class. Write their names in cursive.

Class List

Carl   Emily
Arlene   Otto
Oscar   Adam
Ellen   Carrie

Carl

Emily

Arlene

Otto

Oscar

Adam

Ellen

Carrie

Evaluation

Remember: Capital **A**, **C**, and **E** should be joined to the letters that follow them.

Write the sentences.

Computers make writing more fun for Amy.

_____

_____

_____

_____

Adjust the screen.

_____

_____

Are Oscar and Emily using computer E?

_____

_____

_____

_____

Check Your Handwriting

Do your capital **A**, **C**, and **E** join
the letters that follow them?

Yes   No

☐   ☐

86

Letter, Word, and Sentence Spacing

There should be more space between words than between letters in a word. There should be more space between sentences than between words.

Be careful to space your writing so your tall letters do not run into your descenders. Write the sentences. After each sentence, answer the question.

Arnold plays games on the computer.

Did you use the correct letter spacing?   Yes ☐   No ☐

Aunt Effie uses a computer at work.

Did you use the correct word spacing?   Yes ☐   No ☐

Computers are common. Offices and stores use them.

Did you use the correct sentence spacing?   Yes ☐   No ☐

Writing Cursive H and K

You can see manuscript **H** and **K** in cursive **H** and **K**.
Trace and write the letters.

$\mathcal{H}$ $\mathcal{H}$ $\mathcal{H}$

$\mathcal{K}$ $\mathcal{K}$ $\mathcal{K}$

Trace and write the names of the cities and states.
Join **K** to the letter that follows it, but do not join **H**.

Hi Hat, Kentucky

Hi Hat, Kentucky

Kansas City, Kansas

Kansas City, Kansas

Trace and write the sentences.

Kristy's family went to Kentucky.

Kristy's family went to Kentucky.

Historic sights were seen in Harrodsburg.

Historic sights were seen in Harrodsburg.

Horses were Kristy's favorite sight.

Horses were Kristy's favorite sight.

Writing Cursive N, M, and U

Cursive **N** and **M** look a little like manuscript **N** and
M. Cursive **U** looks very much like manuscript **U**.
Trace and write the letters.

Trace and write the names of the cities and states.
Always join **N, M,** and **U** to the letters that follow them.

Navajo, New Mexico

Navajo, New Mexico

Neely, Mississippi

Neely, Mississippi

Trace and write the sentences.

Neal and Maria visit their family in Utah.

Neal and Maria visit their family in Utah.

Maria loves riding horses with Uncle Ned.

Maria loves riding horses with Uncle Ned.

Neal likes to fish with Uncle Mark.

Neal likes to fish with Uncle Mark.

Writing Cursive V, W, and Y

Cursive **V**, **W**, and **Y** look a little like manuscript **V**, **W**, and **Y**. Trace and write the letters.

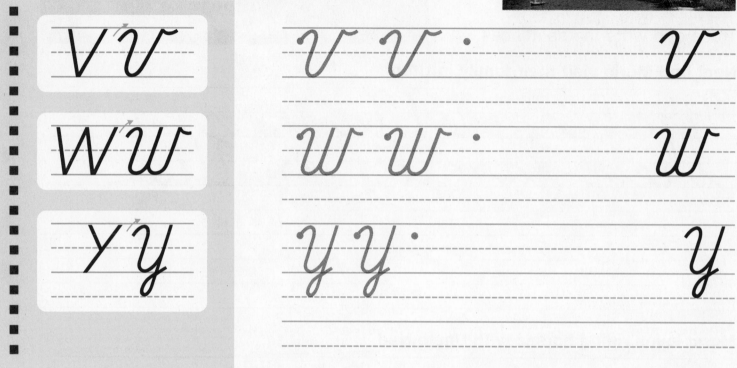

Trace and write the names of the cities and states.
Remember to join cursive **Y** to the letter that follows it, but do not join **V** or **W**.

Yakima, Washington

Yakima, Washington

Van, West Virginia

Van, West Virginia

Trace and write the sentences.

Valerie and Wendy go to national parks.

Valerie and Wendy go to national parks.

Wednesday they left for Yellowstone.

Wednesday they left for Yellowstone.

Valerie's favorite park is Yosemite.

Valerie's favorite park is Yosemite.

Practice

Write the letters.

$\mathcal{H}$

$\mathcal{K}$

$\mathcal{N}$

$\mathcal{M}$

$\mathcal{U}$

$\mathcal{V}$

$\mathcal{W}$

$\mathcal{Y}$

Circle your best letter in each line.

Write the sentence.

Walter Young visited Uncle Ken in Montpelier, Vermont.

94

Review

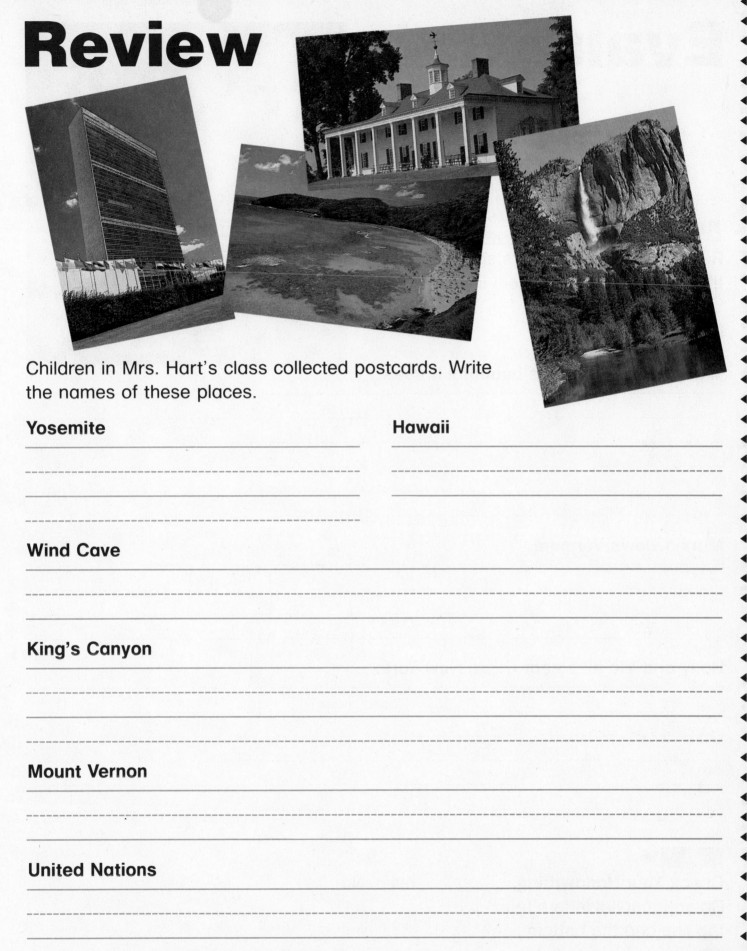

Children in Mrs. Hart's class collected postcards. Write the names of these places.

Yosemite

Hawaii

Wind Cave

King's Canyon

Mount Vernon

United Nations

Evaluation

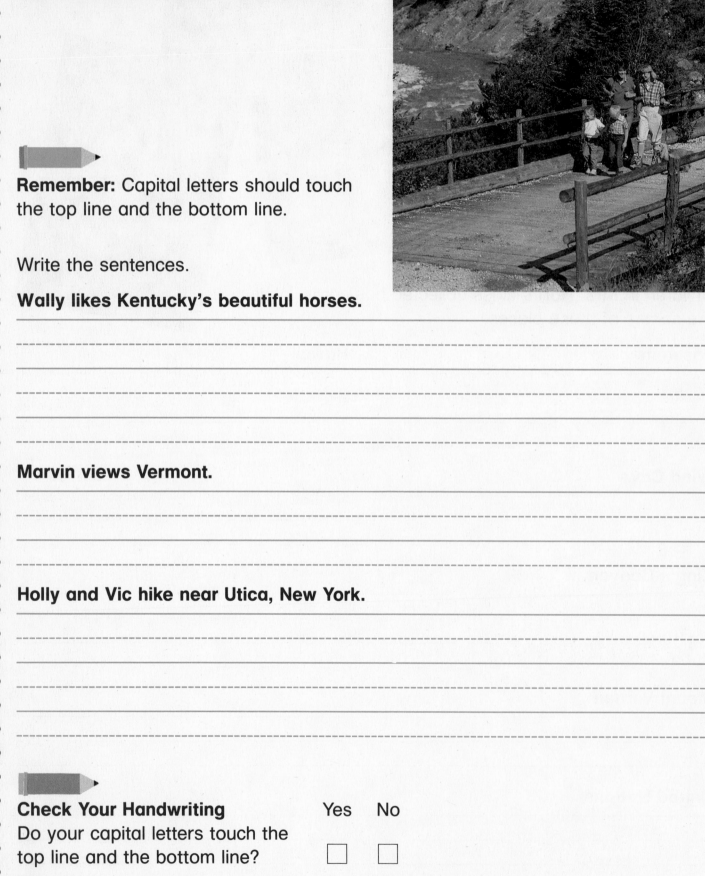

Remember: Capital letters should touch the top line and the bottom line.

Write the sentences.

Wally likes Kentucky's beautiful horses.

Marvin views Vermont.

Holly and Vic hike near Utica, New York.

Check Your Handwriting

Do your capital letters touch the top line and the bottom line?

Yes   No

☐   ☐

Writing a Thank-you Note

Neal wrote a thank-you note to his Uncle Mark when he and his family returned home.

Copy Neal's note on the lines below. Be sure to line up the date and the closing of the note. Make sure you space your words evenly. Try not to let your tall letters touch your descenders as you write.

date ⌐

July 26, 199_

Hi Uncle Mark,
    We had a wonderful time visiting you in Utah. We want to thank you very much.

                Your nephew,
                Neal

closing ⌐

Addressing an Envelope

Neal looked up Uncle Mark's address. Then he addressed the envelope. Notice that Neal did not address the envelope to "Uncle Mark." Use a person's real name on the envelope.

Neal put his return address in the upper left corner of the envelope. When you write an address, remember to use all capital manuscript letters and no punctuation marks. Abbreviate words like *Street* and *Avenue*, and the name of the state.

Copy the addresses on the envelope below. Remember to form your letters clearly and keep your lines straight.

NEAL KOEHLER
609 HAMILTON ST
OMAHA NE 68104

MR. MARK NOVAK
703 WOODLAND AVE
CEDAR VALLEY UT 84013

Reading and Writing

Kate Shelley and the Midnight Express tells about a real girl who lived in 1881. Kate's family lived near the railroad tracks, a creek, and two railroad bridges. One night there was a terrible storm. The bridge over Honey Creek near Kate's house broke, and an engine and two railroad men went down in the creek.

Kate went out in the storm, saw the broken bridge, and heard the men shout for help. Kate wanted to get to the train station to get help and to tell the men to stop the express train. Read the paragraphs from the book that tell what Kate did.

Kate ran along the tracks. Even before she reached the Des Moines River bridge, she could hear the rush of the floodwater. She held up the lantern to light her way over the bridge. But as she did, a fierce wind blew out the lantern's small flame.

Kate stared into the darkness. To reach the Moingona station, she had to cross this river. The long wooden bridge stretched before her. Beside the tracks was a narrow walkway. Some of its boards were missing. There was no handrail to hold.

Kate was afraid to cross this bridge even in daylight. Could she do it now, in this storm, in the dark? Kate thought of the men in Honey Creek. She thought of all the people on the train speeding toward the broken bridge. She got down on her hands and knees and began to crawl across.

Think about someone you know or have read about who has done something courageous. Write some words in the Word Bank below that might help you tell about this person.

Word Bank

_____ _____

_____ _____

_____ _____

_____ _____

_____ _____

_____ _____

Bob decided to write a paragraph about a brave person he knew. He started with these sentences.

Mrs. Wogan saved her daughter from choking. She stayed calm and called 911.

Read what Bob wrote.
	Yes	No
• Did he tell who the brave person is?	☐	☐
• Did he tell what the brave person did?	☐	☐

Proofread Bob's sentences.
	Yes	No
• Did he make his letters the correct size?	☐	☐
• Did he slant all his letters the same way?	☐	☐

Write Bob's sentences on a sheet of paper. Be sure to make your letters the correct size. Remember to slant your letters the same way.

Now it's your turn to write. Tell about someone you know or have read about who has done something courageous. Tell *who* the person is and *what* the person did. You may want to use the words from your Word Bank.

_____

- -

_____

- -

_____

- -

_____

- -

_____

- -

_____

- -

_____

- -

_____

Read your draft carefully.

	Yes	No
• Did you tell who the brave person is?	☐	☐
• Did you tell what the person did?	☐	☐

Proofread your work.

	Yes	No
• Did you make your letters the correct size?	☐	☐
• Did you slant all your letters the same way?	☐	☐

Edit your copy. Then write your revised copy on another sheet of paper.

Writing Cursive T and F

Cursive **T** and **F** look a little like manuscript **T** and **F**.
Trace and write the letters.

Trace and write the proper nouns. **T** and **F** are not
joined to the letters that follow them.

Tallahassee, Florida

Tallahassee, Florida

Tina

Tina

Frank

Frank

Trace and write the sentences.

The Taylors started to recycle in February.

The Taylors started to recycle in February.

Trash day is Friday.

Trash day is Friday.

Tuesday is Trenton's day for bottle pickup.

Tuesday is Trenton's day for bottle pickup.

Writing Cursive B, P, and R

Cursive **B**, **P**, and **R** look like manuscript **B**, **P**, and **R**. Trace and write the letters.

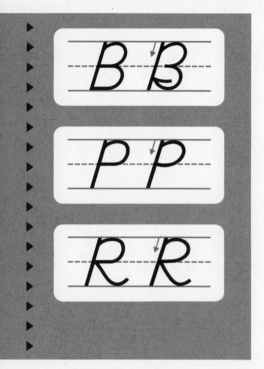

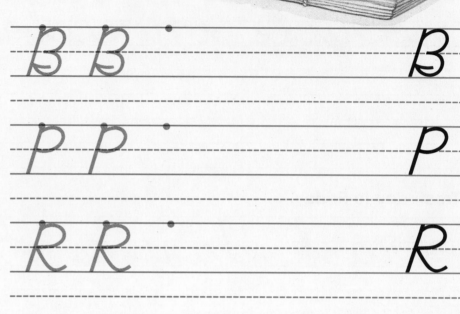

Trace and write the names. Do not join **B** and **P** to the letters that follow them. Always join **R** to the letter that follows it.

Brian

Brian

Paul

Paul

Rita

Rita

Beth

Beth

Trace and write the words in the sign.

Brown's Recycling
and Trash Center
Recycle Paper Products
and Bottles

Practice

Write the letters.

$\mathcal{T}$

$\mathcal{F}$

$\mathcal{B}$

$\mathcal{P}$

$\mathcal{R}$

Circle your best letter in each line.

Write the names of the cities and states.

Paint Rock, Texas

Boca Raton, Florida

Franklin, Tennessee

Berwick, Pennsylvania

Review

Write the names and sentences.

Fran

Rick

Bicycling is Ron's way to save energy.

Plant a tree, Terry.

Turn off water, Flo.

Evaluation

Remember: Leave enough space between words.

Write the sentences.

Bring home your lunch bag, Frannie.

_____

- -

_____

- -

_____

- -

Reuse paper, Patty.

_____

- -

_____

- -

Ted and Barb pick up cans on Fridays.

_____

- -

_____

- -

_____

- -

Check Your Handwriting

Did you leave enough space between words?

Yes ☐   No ☐

108

Writing Punctuation Marks

A question is a sentence that asks something. It begins with a capital letter and ends with a **question mark.** Trace and write the question marks.

? ? ?

Sentences that show strong feelings are exclamations. They end with **exclamation marks.** Trace and write the exclamation marks.

! ! !

Quotation marks are used to show a speaker's exact words. Notice that the quotation marks at the beginning of a sentence go in a different direction from the quotation marks at the end. Trace and write the quotation marks.

" " "   *" " "*

Copy the following sentences. Be sure to slant all the punctuation marks the same way you slant your letters.

"What a mess!" said Ana. "Who can help?"

Writing a Telephone Message

Sometimes you answer the phone for someone else. You may have to take a message. Look at the message Brittany wrote for her brother Ryan. It gives all the important information. The message is neat and clearly written.

Brittany's paper does not have middle lines. Imagine a middle line as you write to help you keep your letters the correct size. Copy Brittany's telephone message on the lines below.

Telephone Message

To: *Ryan,*

Message: *Mrs. Morrow called at 8:00 P.M. The scouts will meet at Elm Park tomorrow at 10:00 A.M. to collect bottles. Please call her at 964-1789 if you can't be there.*

From: *Brittany*

Telephone Message

To:

Message:

From:

Writing Abbreviations

An abbreviation is a shortened form of a word. Abbreviations are useful when writing signs, posters, letters, and messages. Abbreviations begin with a capital letter and end with a period. Look at the dates and names below.

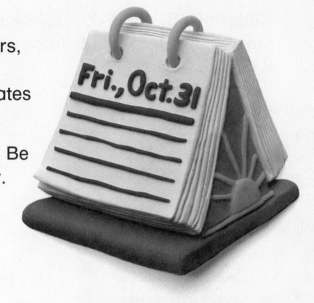

Write just the abbreviations in cursive handwriting. Be sure your letters and numbers slant the same way.

Friday, February 14   **Fri., Feb. 14**

Tuesday, August 19   **Tues., Aug. 19**

Friday, October 31   **Fri., Oct. 31**

Monday, November 17   **Mon., Nov. 17**

Mister Martin Running Bear   **Mr. M. Running Bear**

Tiffany Rebecca Fuller   **T. R. Fuller**

Writing Cursive G, S, and I

Cursive **G**, **S**, and **I** do not look like manuscript **G**, **S**, and **I**. Trace and write the letters.

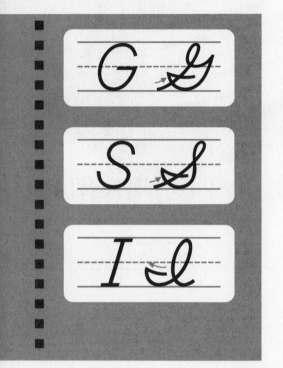

Trace and write the names. Do not join **G** and **S** to the letters that follow them. Always join **I** to the letter that follows it. Remember that the pronoun **I** is always capitalized.

Galileo

Galileo

Gemini

Gemini

Sir Isaac Newton

Sir Isaac Newton

Trace and write the sentences.

Gloria and Ingrid studied the planets.

Gloria and Ingrid studied the planets.

Sarah and I reported on Saturn's rings.

Sarah and I reported on Saturn's rings.

Spaceships interested both Greg and Ivan.

Spaceships interested both Greg and Ivan.

Writing Cursive Q, Z, and D

Cursive **Q** and **Z** do not look like manuscript **Q** and **Z**.
Cursive **D** looks something like manuscript **D**. Trace
and write the letters.

$Q \, 2$ $2 \; 2 \; \cdot$ 2

$Z \, z$ $z \; z \; \cdot$ z

$D \, D$ $D \; D \; \cdot$ D

Trace and write names of the constellations. Always
join cursive **Q** and **Z** to the letters that follow them,
but do not join cursive **D**.

Dorado

Dorado

Draco

Draco

Several students in Mr. Dennison's class wrote a report about the Space Shuttle *Discovery*. They all signed their names under the title. Trace and write the title and the names.

Space Shuttle Discovery
Zack   Quan
Debbie   Zoe
Zelda   Diana
Dick   Quinn

Space Shuttle
Discovery
Zack   Quan
Debbie   Zoe
Zelda   Diana
Dick   Quinn

Writing Cursive J, X, and L

Cursive **J** does not look like manuscript **J**. You can see cursive **X** in manuscript **X**. Cursive **L** looks something like manuscript **L**. Trace and write the letters.

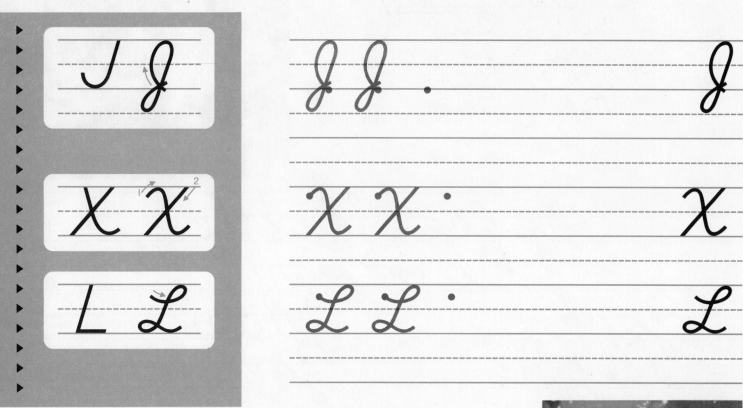

Trace and write the sentence. Always join **J** and **L** to the letters that follow them, but do not join **X**.

Jim Lovell was a Gemini astronaut.

Jim Lovell was a Gemini astronaut.

Trace and write the sentences.

X-ray telescopes can help astronomers.

X-ray telescopes can help astronomers.

Jupiter is the largest planet.

Jupiter is the largest planet.

Libra is a constellation.

Libra is a constellation.

Practice

Write the letters.

$\mathcal{G}$

$\mathcal{S}$

$\mathcal{L}$

$\mathcal{Q}$

$\mathcal{Z}$

$\mathcal{D}$

$\mathcal{I}$

$\mathcal{X}$

$\mathcal{L}$

Circle your best letter in each line.

Write the name.

Goddard Space Flight Center

Review

Write the names.

Gail

_____
- - - - - - - - - - - - - - - - -
_____

Sue

_____
- - - - - - - - - - - - - - - - -
_____

Ira

_____
- - - - - - - - - - - - - - - - -
_____

Xavier

_____
- - - - - - - - - - - - - - - - -
_____

Louis

_____
- - - - - - - - - - - - - - - - -
_____

Dana

_____
- - - - - - - - - - - - - - - - -
_____

Jenny

_____
- - - - - - - - - - - - - - - - -
_____

Quincy

_____
- - - - - - - - - - - - - - - - -
_____

Zack

_____
- - - - - - - - - - - - - - - - -
_____

Evaluation

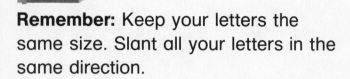

Remember: Keep your letters the same size. Slant all your letters in the same direction.

Write the sentences.

Did you visit the Johnson Space Center?

_____

- -

_____

- -

_____

- -

Quinn, Zoe, and Inez studied X-ray stars.

_____

- -

_____

- -

_____

- -

Larry and Ginny are studying Saturn.

_____

- -

_____

- -

_____

- -

Check Your Handwriting

	Yes	No
Are your letters the same size?	☐	☐
Do your letters slant in the same direction?	☐	☐

Writing Names of Planets

The names of the planets are proper nouns. They begin
with capital letters. Write the names of the planets in cursive.
Try not to let your tall letters touch your descenders.

1. _____ 6. _____

2. _____ 7. _____

3. _____ 8. _____

4. _____ 9. _____

5. _____

Write the sentence.

The sun, planets, and moons make up the solar system.

_____

_____

_____

_____

Making a Chart

Children in Mrs. Esposito's class were very interested in the astronauts. They studied the Mercury, Gemini, Apollo, and Space Shuttle astronauts. Then they made a chart of important dates in space.

Look at their chart on the next page. Copy the chart in manuscript handwriting on the form below. Be sure to adjust the size of your handwriting to fit the space.

Important Dates in Space

Important Dates in Space

Date	Event
May 5, 1961	Alan Shepard is the first American in space.
Feb. 20, 1962	John Glenn is the first American to orbit Earth.
June 5, 1965	Edward White is the first person to "walk" in space.
July 20, 1969	Neil Armstrong and Edwin Aldrin are the first to land on the moon.
April 12, 1981	Space Shuttle <u>Columbia</u> makes its first flight into space.
June 18, 1983	Sally Ride is the first American woman in space.
Aug. 30, 1983	Guion S. Bluford, Jr. is the first African American in space.

Signing an Autograph Book

Sometimes you write on paper that has no lines at all. Then you have to be careful to keep your lines of handwriting straight. Make sure you leave enough space between your letters and words.

Copy one of the rhymes in the autograph book below. Remember to sign your name below the rhyme.

RHYMES...

East is East.
West is West.
This is the verse
That I like best.

I am no astronaut,
I have no fame,
But just the same
I'll sign my name.

FRIENDS

Reading and Writing

The book *Company's Coming* by Arthur Yorinks tells a story about a flying saucer that landed in Moe and Shirley's backyard. Two visitors from outer space walked out of the saucer.

Read these paragraphs from the story to see how Moe and Shirley reacted to their unexpected visitors.

On the day Shirley had invited all of her relatives to dinner and Moe, her husband, was pleasantly tinkering in the yard, a flying saucer quietly landed next to their toolshed. Moe was surprised.

"Shirley!" he yelled.

Shirley joined Moe on the patio.

"Moe, you had to buy that barbecue? It's too big," she complained.

"Shirl, it's not a barbecue," Moe said.

Suddenly, a small hatch on the saucer opened and out walked two visitors from outer space.

"Greetings," they spoke in English. "We come in peace. Do you have a bathroom?"

Stunned, Shirley replied, "Down the hall and to the left." The foreigners nodded graciously and walked into the house.

"How could you let them into our house!" Moe was upset.

"Did you see those helmets? Those ray guns? They'll vaporize us!" Moe was very upset.

"Shhush, they're coming," Shirley whispered. "Stay calm. Be polite. Maybe we can make friends with them." ■

If you could take a trip in a flying saucer, what would
you want to see? Why would you like to see it?
Make a list of things you would want to see and why.

_____

_____

_____

_____

_____

_____

Pat wrote a few paragraphs about why she would
like to find life on another planet. She wrote these
sentences to start her story.

*It would be great
to meet people from
another planet. I
wonder what kinds of
machines they use.*

Read what Pat wrote.   Yes   No
- Did she tell what she would like to see?   ☐   ☐
- Did she tell why she would like to see it?   ☐   ☐

Proofread Pat's sentences.
- Are her letters joined correctly?   ☐   ☐

Write Pat's sentences on a sheet of paper. Be sure to
join your letters correctly.

126

Choose the most interesting thing from the list you made on page 126. Write about it. Tell why you would like to see it.

_____

- -

_____

- -

_____

- -

_____

- -

_____

- -

_____

- -

_____

- -

_____

- -

Read your draft carefully.
- Did you tell what you would like to see?
- Did you tell why you would like to see it?

Yes No

Proofread your work.
- Are all your letters joined correctly?

Edit your copy. Then write the revised copy on another sheet of paper.

127

Index

Abbreviations, 51, 98, 111
Adjusting handwriting
   size, 23, 41, 51, 57, 58, 110, 122–123
   tall letters and descenders, 50, 78, 87, 97, 121
   without writing lines, 23, 51, 58, 98, 122–123, 124
Authors, 59
Autograph book, signing on, 124
Capitalization
   of abbreviations, 111
   of addresses on envelopes, 51, 98
   of pronoun *I*, 112
   of proper nouns, 80, 121
Chart, making a, 122–123
Common-stroke letter groups, manuscript
   aA, dD, oO, gG, 13
   cC, eE, sS, 14
   fF, bB, IL, 15
   tT, hH, kK, 16
   iI, uU, wW, yY, 17
   jJ, rR, nN, mM, pP, 18
   qQ, vV, zZ, xX, 19
Cursive handwriting
   capitals, 80–97, 102–121
   joining strokes, 25–28, 66–67
     ending, 25, 26
     overhill, 26, 27, 28, 42, 44, 46
     sidestroke, 27, 28, 52, 60, 66–67
     uphill, 25, 28, 32, 34, 36
   lower-case, 32–40, 42–50, 52–57, 60–70
Descenders, 8, 30, 50, 78, 87, 97, 121. *See also* Adjusting handwriting
Envelope, addressing an, 98
Evaluating handwriting, 8, 9, 22, 31, 38, 40, 48, 50, 54, 56, 68, 70, 74–75, 84, 86, 94, 96, 100–101, 106, 108, 118, 120, 126–127. *See also* Legibility
Evaluation, 22, 40, 50, 56, 70, 86, 96, 108, 120. *See also* Legibility
Everyday writing
   autograph book, 124
   chart, 122–123
   envelope, 98
   form, 41
   list, 12, 57
   paragraph, 76
   postcard, 51
   poster, 58
   punctuation, 109
   schedule, 23
   telephone message, 110
   thank-you note, 97
   time, 71
   titles and authors, 59
Form, filling out a, 41
I, **capitalization of,** 112

Joining Strokes. *See* Cursive handwriting
Legibility
   letter, word, and sentence spacing, 9, 31, 59, 87, 97, 108, 124
   letter size and form, 8, 23, 30, 74–75, 78, 100–101, 110, 122
   letter slant, 9, 22, 31, 79, 100–101, 109, 111
Letters
   cursive capitals
     A, 80; B, 104; C, 80; D, 114; E, 82; F, 102; G, 112; H, 88; I, 112; J, 116; K, 88; L, 116; M, 90; N, 90; O, 82; P, 104; Q, 114; R, 104; S, 112; T, 102; U, 90; V, 92; W, 92; X, 116; Y, 92; Z, 114
   cursive lower-case
     a, 42; b, 52; c, 42; d, 42; e, 34; f, 64; g, 46; h, 32; i, 34; j, 36; k, 32; l, 32; m, 44; n, 44; o, 52; p, 36; q, 46; r, 62; s, 62; t, 32; u, 34; v, 60; w, 52; x, 44; y, 46; z, 60
   manuscript
     aA, 13; bB, 15; cC, 14; dD, 13; eE, 14; fF, 15; gG, 13; hH, 16; iI, 17; jJ, 18; kK, 16; lL, 15; mM, 18; nN, 18; oO, 13; pP, 18; qQ, 19; rR, 18; sS, 14; tT, 16; uU, 17; vV, 19; wW, 17; xX, 19; yY, 17; zZ, 19
Letter size and form, 8, 30, 78
Letter slant, 9, 31, 79, 109
Letter spacing, 9, 31, 87
List, writing a, 12, 57
Maintaining manuscript, 41, 51, 58, 59, 76, 98, 122–123
Numbers, 12
Number words, writing, 71, 72, 76
Paragraph, writing numbers in a, 76
Position for writing, 6–7
Postcard, writing a, 51
Poster, making a, 58
Practice, 20, 38, 48, 54, 68, 84, 94, 106, 118
Proper nouns, 80, 82, 102, 121
Punctuation marks
   comma, 80
   exclamation marks, 109
   period, 111
   question mark, 109
   quotation marks, 109
   underlining, 59
Reading and writing, 73–75, 99–101, 125–127
Review, 21, 39, 49, 55, 69, 85, 95, 107, 119
Schedule, making a, 23
Sentence spacing, 87
Telephone message, writing a, 110
Thank-you note, writing a, 97
Time, writing, 71
Titles and authors, writing, 59
Transition to cursive, 10, 24–28
Word spacing, 31, 87, 97, 108, 124
Writing. *See* Reading and writing

128